Ten Parish Settings

PATRICK APPLEFORD
MALCOLM ARCHER
GRAHAM ELLIOTT COLIN MAWBY
HARRISON OXLEY
DOM ALAN REES ALAN RIDOUT
DAVID SAINT
CHRISTOPHER TAMBLING

Kevin Mayhew

We hope you enjoy the music in this book. Further copies are available
from your local music shop or Christian bookshop.

In case of difficulty, please contact the publisher direct by writing to:

The Sales Department
KEVIN MAYHEW LTD
Rattlesden
Bury St Edmunds
Suffolk
IP30 0SZ

Phone 0449 737978
Fax 0449 737834

Please ask for our complete catalogue of outstanding Church Music.

First published in Great Britain in 1994 by Kevin Mayhew Ltd

ISBN 0 86209 520 4
Catalogue No: 1450017

Front Cover: *Stoke Poges Church* by Jasper Francis Cropsey (1823-1900).
Reproduced by courtesy of Johnny van Haeften Gallery, London/
Bridegman Art Library, London.
Cover design by Juliette Clarke and Graham Johnstone.
Picture Research: Jane Rayson

Printed and bound in Great Britain

Contents

About the Composers

PATRICK APPLEFORD is one of England's best known hymn writers. His *Living Lord* (Lord Jesus Christ) is included in all the major hymn books.

MALCOLM ARCHER, formerly Organist and Master of the Choristers at Bristol Cathedral, is a recitalist, composer and conductor.

GRAHAM ELLIOTT is Organist and Master of the Music at Chelmsford Cathedral, where he also founded and directs the annual Cathedral Festival. He is a Professor at the Guildhall School of Music.

COLIN MAWBY is Choral Director at Radio Telefís Éireann, the national broadcasting authority in the Republic of Ireland. He was previously Master of the Music at Westminster Cathedral.

HARRISON OXLEY was formerly Organist of St Edmundsbury Cathedral for 26 years. He is well known as a composer, recitalist and adjudicator. He is Director of the St Edmundsbury Bach Choir and St Cecilia Singers.

DOM ALAN REES was formerly Abbot of the Benedictine community at Belmont, near Hereford. His music has made a significant contribution to many of the national events in the life of the Roman Catholic church in Great Britain.

ALAN RIDOUT is one of England's most prolific composers, having composed music in almost every form: symphonies, chamber music, choral and instrumental works. His choral and organ music, in particular, is widely performed by church and cathedral choirs.

DAVID SAINT is Organist and Master of the Music at St Chad's Cathedral, Birmingham. In addition to his work with the Cathedral Choir, he also teaches in the School of Music at Birmingham Polytechnic.

CHRISTOPHER TAMBLING was Organ Scholar of St Peter's College, and Organist and Choir Master at Pusey House, Oxford. He is now the Director of Music at Glenalmond College in Perthshire.

THE HADLEIGH SETTING

Alan Ridout

KYRIE

GLORIA

glo - ry. Lord Je - sus Christ, on - ly Son of the Fa - ther.

Lord _____ God, Lamb _ of God, you take _ a - way _ the sin of the

world: _____ have mer - cy on us; you are seat - ed at _ the

right hand of the Fa - ther: re - ceive our prayer. For

you_ a - lone are the Ho - ly One, you a - lone are_ the

Lord,_____ you a - lone are_ the Most High,_____

Je - sus Christ, with the Ho - ly Spi - rit, in the glo - ry of

God_ the Fa - ther. A - men._____

SANCTUS

ACCLAMATIONS

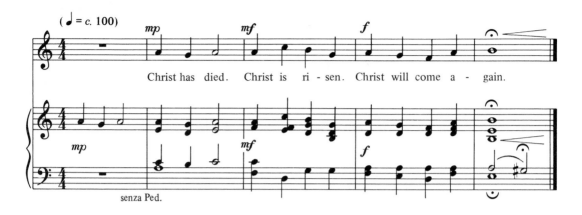

Christ has died. Christ is ri - sen. Christ will come a - gain.

GREAT AMEN

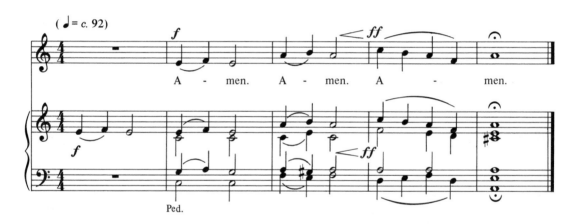

A - men. A - men. A - men.

AGNUS DEI

Lamb of God, you take a - way the

sins of the world:__ have mer - cy on us. __

Lamb __ of God, you take __ a - way the sins of the world: __ have

mer - cy on us. __ Lamb __ of God, you take __ a -

way the sins of the world: __ grant us peace.

THE HOLY TRINITY SERVICE

Christopher Tambling

KYRIE

GLORIA

Glo-ry to God in the high-est, and peace to his peo-ple on earth.

Lord God, heav'n-ly King, al - migh - ty God and Fa - ther, we

wor-ship you, we give you thanks, we praise you for __ your glo-ry.

Lord Je-sus Christ, on-ly Son of the Fa - ther, Lord God, Lamb of God,

you take a-way the sin of the world; have mer-cy on us:

you are seat-ed at the right hand of God the Fa-ther: re -

ceive our prayer. For

you a-lone are the Ho-ly One, you a-lone are the Lord,

you a-lone are the Most High, Je-sus Christ, with the Ho-ly Spi-rit, in the

glo-ry of God the Fa-ther. A-men, A - men.

A - men, A - men.

(L.H.)
+ Gt. reeds

+ pedal
reeds etc.

(Ped.)

THE GOSPEL

THANKSGIVING

SANCTUS

Ho-ly, ho-ly, ho-ly Lord, God of_ power and might, heav'n and earth are full of your glo-ry. Ho-san-na in the high-est.

Bles-sed is he who comes in the name of the Lord. Ho - san - na in the high - est, Ho - san - na in the high - est!

ACCLAMATIONS

GREAT AMEN

18

AGNUS DEI

Je - sus, Lamb of God: _____ have mer-cy on us.

Je - sus, bear-er of our sins: have mer-cy on us. _____

Je - sus, re-deem-er of the world: give us your peace.

DISMISSAL

In the name of Christ, A-men, A - men!

Go in peace to love and serve the Lord

THE CHELMSFORD SETTING

Graham Elliott

KYRIE

GLORIA

Lord Jesus Christ, only Son of the Father, Lord God, Lamb of God, you take a-way the sin of the world: have mer-cy on us; you are seat-ed at the right hand of the Fa-ther: re-ceive our prayer. For

SANCTUS

san - na in the high - est.

Bles - sed is he who comes in the

name of the Lord. Ho - san - na in the high -

est, ho - san - na in the high - est.

AGNUS DEI

Lamb_ of God, you Man.

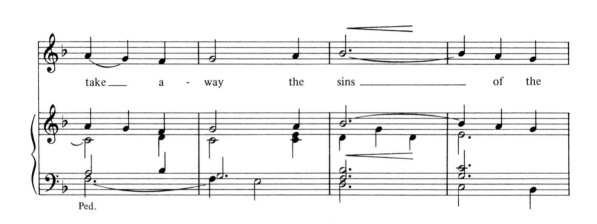

take_ a - way the sins _____ of the Ped.

world: have mer - cy on us. Lamb_ of

God, you take a - way the sins

of the world: have mer - cy on us.

Lamb of God, you take a - way the

sins of the world: grant us peace.

THE NORTH ELMHAM SETTING

Colin Mawby

KYRIE

GLORIA

Glo-ry to God in the high-est, and peace to his peo-ple on earth.

S.
A.

Glo-ry to God in the high-est, and peace to his peo-ple on earth, on earth.

T.
B.

Ped.

Slower (still in 2)

Lord Je-sus Christ, on-ly Son of the Fa-ther, Lord God,

Lord Je-sus Christ, on-ly Son of the Fa-ther, Lord God,

Lamb of God, you take a - way the sin of the world: have mer - cy

Lamb of God, you take a - way the sin of the world: have mer - cy

on us; you are seat - ed at the right hand, the

on us; you are seat - ed at the right hand, the

right hand of the Fa - ther: re - ceive our prayer, our

right hand of the Fa - ther: re - ceive our prayer, our

Tempo 1

prayer. For you a - lone are the Ho - ly One,

prayer. For you a - lone are the Ho - ly ___ One,

Man.

you a - lone are the Lord, you a - lone are the Most High,

you a - lone are the Lord, you a - lone are the Most __ High, __

Je-sus Christ, with the Ho - ly Spi-rit, in the glo-ry of God the Fa - ther.

Je-sus Christ, with the Ho - ly Spi-rit, in the glo-ry of God the Fa - ther.

mf

f

Ped.

* optional high A

34

THE GOSPEL

When it is announced:

At the conclusion:

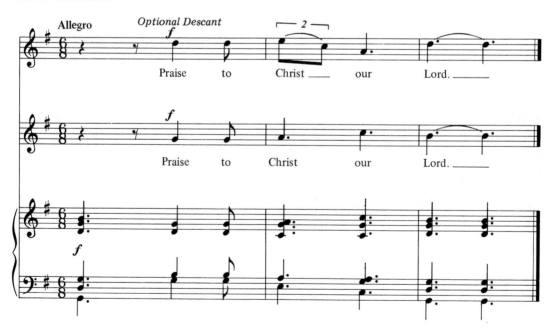

SANCTUS

ACCLAMATIONS

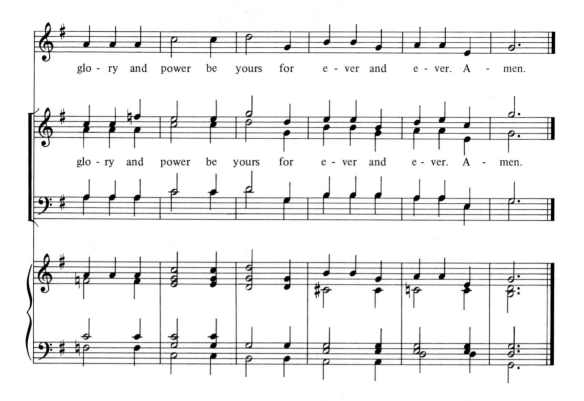

glo - ry and power be yours for e - ver and e - ver. A - men.

glo - ry and power be yours for e - ver and e - ver. A - men.

GREAT AMEN

A - men, A - men.

A - men, A - men.

Man.

AGNUS DEI

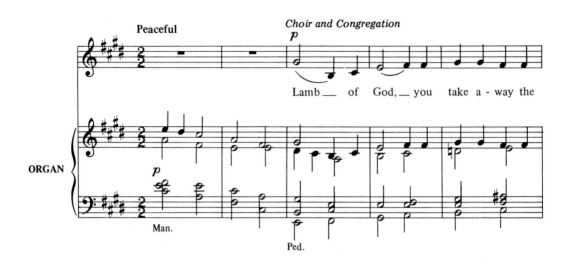

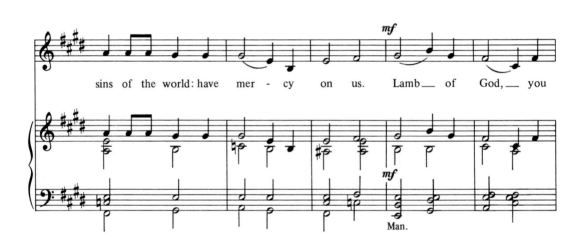

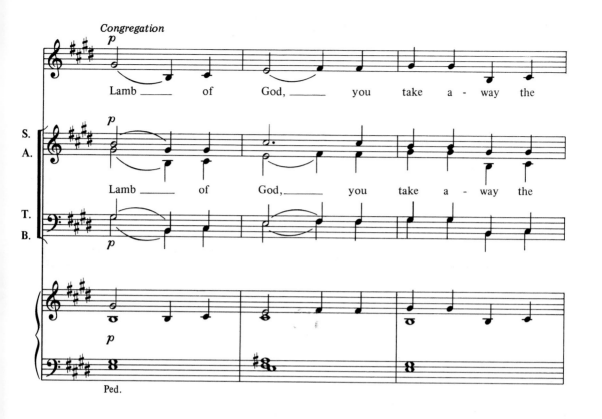

Congregation

Lamb of God, you take a - way the

S.
A.

Lamb of God, you take a - way the

T.
B.

Ped.

sins of the world: grant us peace.

pp grant us peace.

sins of the world: grant us peace.

41

DISMISSAL

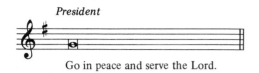

President

Go in peace and serve the Lord.

Maestoso   *Congregation*

In the name of Christ. A - men, A - men.

S.
A.

In the name of Christ. A - men, A - men.

T.
B.

THE ST ALBANS SETTING

Malcolm Archer

KYRIE

* Optional Soprano Descant

GLORIA

* The Congregation sing the Soprano part.

Glo - ry to God in the high - est, and_ peace to his peo - ple on earth.

Lord Je - sus Christ, on-ly Son of the Fa - ther, Lord God, Lamb of God: you take a-way the

sin of the world: have mer - cy on us; you are seat- ed at the right hand of the

with the Ho - ly Spi - rit, in the glo - ry of God, the_ Fa - ther,

Glo - ry to God in the high - est, and_ peace to his peo - ple on earth.

A - men.

A - men, A - men, A - men.

THE GOSPEL

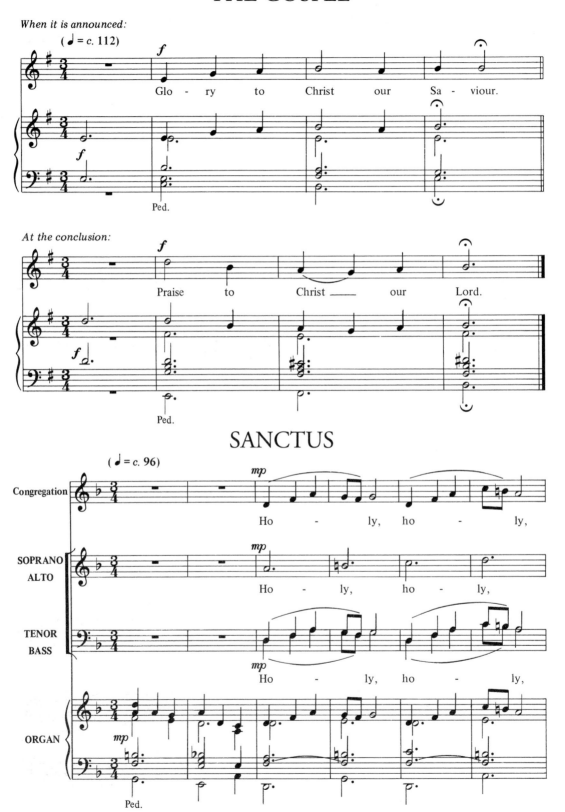

When it is announced:

Glo - ry to Christ our Sa - viour.

At the conclusion:

Praise to Christ ____ our Lord.

SANCTUS

Congregation: Ho - ly, ho - ly,

Ho - ly, ho - ly,

Ho - ly, ho - ly,

BENEDICTUS

ACCLAMATIONS

AGNUS DEI

1st time: choir only in harmony
2nd time: all in unison (apart from last chord in harmony)

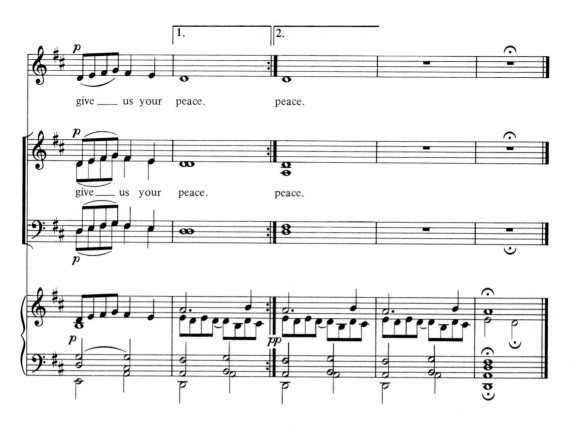

give ___ us your peace.   peace.

give ___ us your peace.   peace.

DISMISSAL

(♩ = c. 92)

Congregation

In the name of Christ. A - men.

S.
A.

In the name of Christ. A - men.

T.

President

Go in peace to love and serve the Lord.

B.

Man.   Ped.

MASS FOR ALL SEASONS

Patrick Appleford

KYRIE

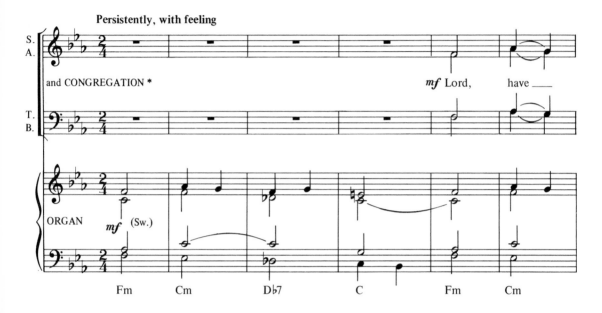

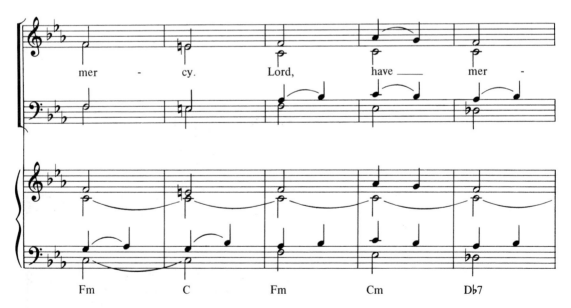

* Congregation sing the soprano part throughout this setting,
except where indicated at the end of the Sanctus.

GLORIA

One, you a lone are the Lord, you a - lone are the Most

G   C   F   Dm7   Dm   C7   G   Em7

High, Je - sus Christ,___ with the Ho - ly Spi - rit in the glo — ry of

Am G Dm7 F7 Dm7   C   G   C

God, the Fa - ther. A - men.___

F   C   G7   C

SANCTUS

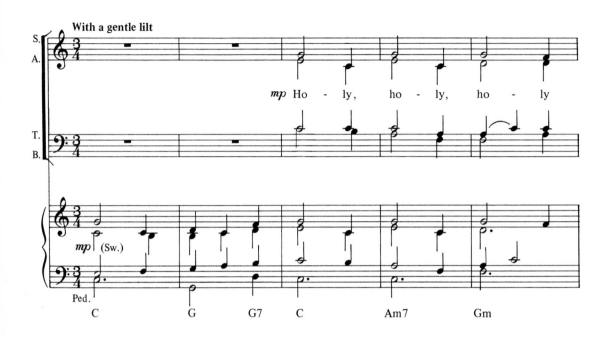

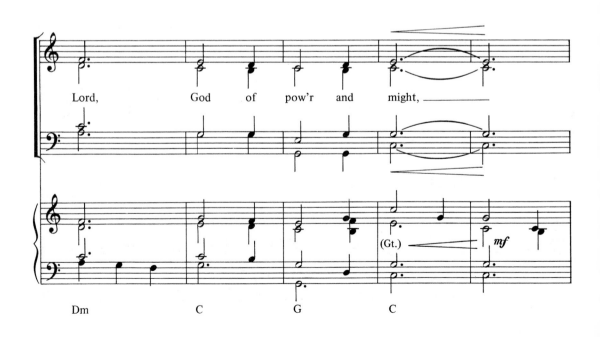

61

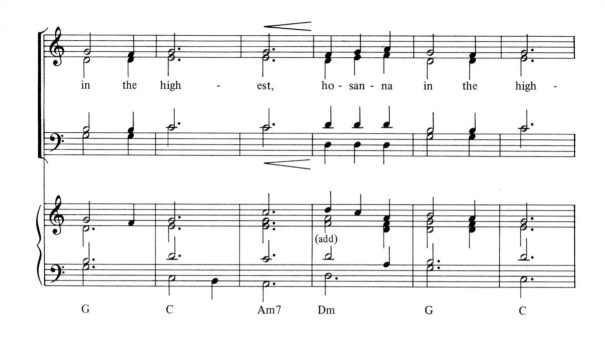

in the high - est, ho - san - na in the high -

G   C   Am7   Dm   G   C

CONGREGATION

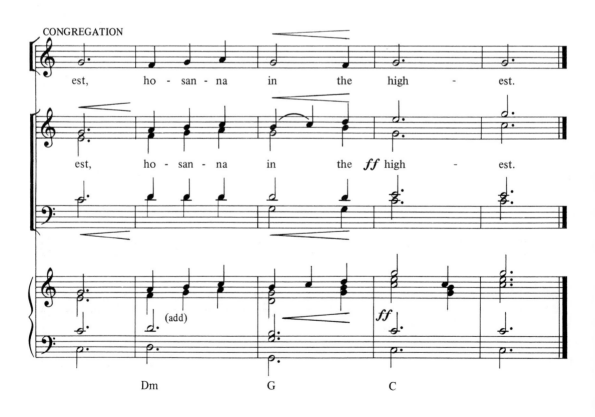

est, ho - san - na in the high - est.

est, ho - san - na in the *ff* high - est.

Dm   G   C

ACCLAMATIONS

Christ has died, Christ is ri - sen, Christ will come a - gain.

A - men, a - men, a - men.

AGNUS DEI

For Geoffrey Hannant

THE ST JOHN'S SERVICE

Harrison Oxley

KYRIE

* The choir may be SATB, SA or Sopranos only. If there is no choir, the choir part could be given to a soloist; alternatively, the congregation could sing throughout.

Christ, __ have mer - cy. Lord, __ have mer - cy. Lord, __

Lord, __ have mer - cy. Lord, __

Lord, __ have mer - cy.

Lord, __ have mer - cy.

GLORIA

* If there is no choir or soloist, it may be preferable here and in the following section for the organist to play
from the choir staves.

you take a - way____ the sin____ of the world: have mer - cy on

you take a - way____ the sin____ of the world:

you take a - way the sin of the world: have mer - cy on

you take a - way____ the sin of the world:

Gt. *mp*

Ped.

us; ____ you are seat - ed at the right hand of the Fa - ther:

us; ____ you are seat - ed at the right hand of the Fa - ther:

Sw. *mp*

Man.

Christ, with the Ho - ly Spi - rit, in the glo - ry of God

Christ, with the Ho - ly Spi - rit, in the glo - ry of God

the Fa - ther. A - men.

God the Fa - ther. A - men.

THE GOSPEL

When it is announcea:

(𝅗𝅥 = 80)

Choir and Congregation

f

Glo - ry to Christ our ___ Sa - viour.

ORGAN

f

Ped.

At the conclusion:

f

Praise to Christ our ___ Lord.

f

non legato

ALTERNATIVE FOR BAS (CANADA) *Choir and Congregation*

(𝅗𝅥 = 80)

f

Glo - ry to you, Lord Je - sus ___ Christ.

ORGAN

f

Ped.

f

Praise to you, Lord Je - sus ___ Christ.

f

non legato

THE EUCHARISTIC PRAYER

74

SANCTUS

* If this setting is sung by choir only, for these two bars most or all of the sopranos should sing the
congregation part.

glo - ry. Ho - san - na, Ho - san - na in the high - est, the

glo - ry. Ho - san - na, Ho - san - na in the high - est, the

high - est.

high - est.

OMIT THIS BAR
if continuing into
BENEDICTUS

BENEDICTUS

† In the absence of an SATB choir, the organist plays the small notes.

ACCLAMATIONS

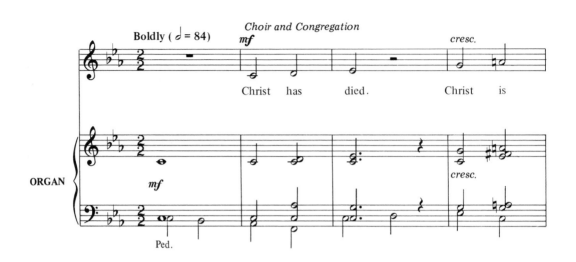

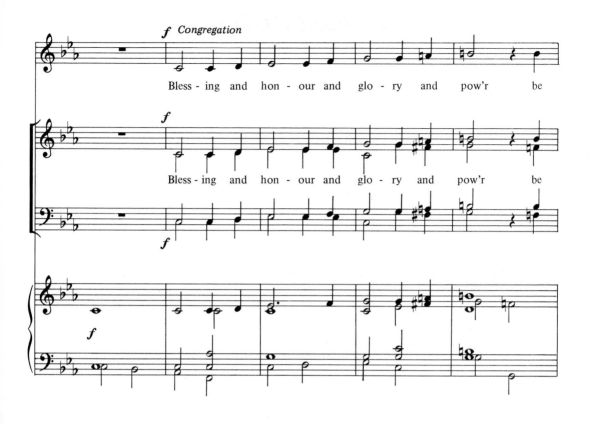

Bless - ing and hon - our and glo - ry and pow'r be

Bless - ing and hon - our and glo - ry and pow'r be

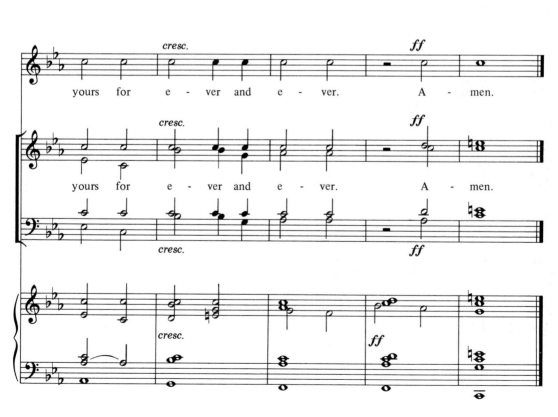

yours for e - ver and e - ver. A - men.

yours for e - ver and e - ver. A - men.

AGNUS DEI

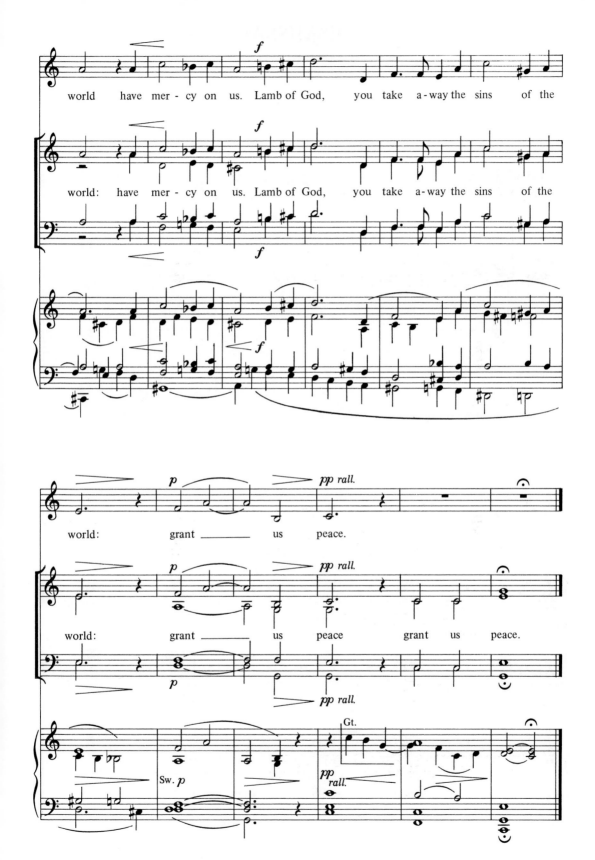

world have mer - cy on us. Lamb of God, you take a - way the sins of the

world: have mer - cy on us. Lamb of God, you take a - way the sins of the

world: grant _____ us peace.

world: grant _____ us peace grant us peace.

DISMISSAL

Colorado Springs, October 1989

THE USHAW SETTING

Dom Alan Rees

KYRIE

GLORIA

glo - ry to God, glo - ry to God in the high - est.

Lord God, hea - ven - ly King, al - migh - ty God __ and

Optional descant

We wor - ship you, we give __ you thanks, and

Fa - ther, we wor - ship you, we give __ you thanks, we

praise _____ for your glo - ry.

praise you __ for your glo - ry. *f* All Glo - ry, glo - ry to God,

glo - ry to God in the high - est. *mp* Choir Lord Je - sus Christ,

Lord God, Lamb of God,

on - ly Son of the Fa - ther, Lord God Lamb of God,

you take a-way the sin of the world: have mer-cy on us; ___ you are

seat - ed at the right hand of the Fa - ther: re -

ceive our prayer. Glo - ry,

glo - ry to God, glo - ry to God in the high - est. For

SANCTUS

* The choir may sing in harmony by doubling the **organ** part at sections marked "Optional harmony".

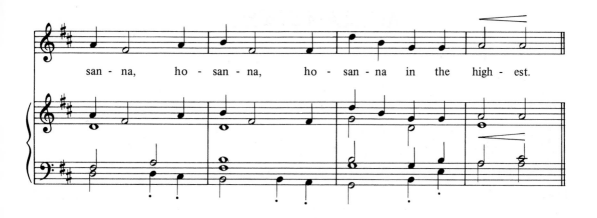

san - na, ho - san - na, ho - san - na in the high - est.

mp Choir
Bless - ed is he who comes in the name of the

mp
Optional harmony

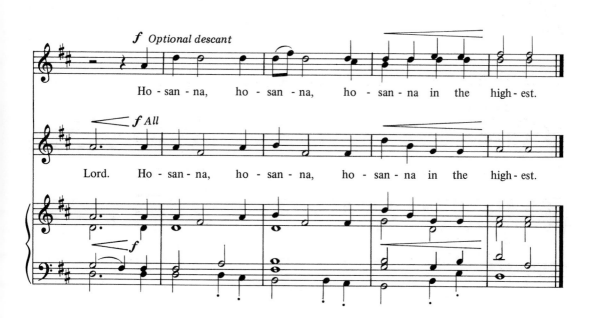

f Optional descant
Ho - san - na, ho - san - na, ho - san - na in the high - est.

f All
Lord. Ho - san - na, ho - san - na, ho - san - na in the high - est.

f

ACCLAMATIONS

Christ has died,

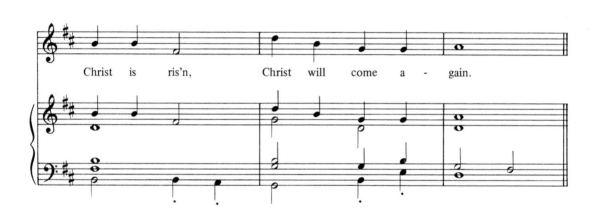

Christ is ris'n, Christ will come a - gain.

Bless - ing and hon - our and

glo - ry and power be yours for ev - er and ev - er. A - men.

Optional descant

f

A - men.

VOICES

f All

A - men.

ORGAN *mf*

A - men.

A - men.

A - men.

A - men.

A - men.

AGNUS DEI

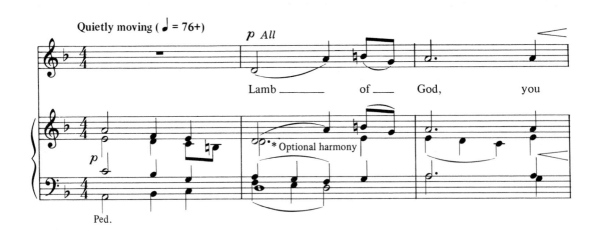

Lamb _____ of __ God, you

take a - way the sins of the world: have mer - cy on us.

Optional descant

Lamb __ of God, you __ take a - way the

Lamb _____ of God, you take a - way the

* The choir may sing in harmony by doubling the organ part at sections marked "Optional harmony".

sins___ of the world, have mer - cy on us.

sins of the world, have mer - cy on us.

Lamb _____ of ___ God, you take a - way the

grant _____ us peace.

sins of the world, grant _____ us ___ peace.

For C.M.

THE ST CHAD'S SETTING

David Saint

KYRIE

* The Congregation sing the melody throughout this setting, except where indicated.

GLORIA

peo - ple on earth. *mp* Lord God, hea - ven - ly King, al - migh - ty God and Fa - ther, *mf* we wor - ship you, we give you thanks, we praise you for your glo - ry.

Man.

Ped.

99

1st time *Choir*, 2nd time *All*

f Glo - ry to God, God in the high - est, peace to his peo - ple, his peo - ple on earth.

peo - ple on earth. *p* Lord Je - sus Christ, on - ly Son of the Fa - ther,

prayer.

mf

f

1st time *Choir*, 2nd time *All*

f Glo - ry to God, God in the high-est, peace to his peo-ple his

1. peo - ple on earth.
2. peo - ple on earth.

mf For you a - lone are the

Choir

1.
2.

f

mf (Unaccompanied ad lib.)

Ho - ly One, you a - lone are the Lord, ___ you a - lone are the Most High, Je - sus Christ, Je -. sus Christ, with the Ho - ly Spi - rit, in the glo - ry of

senza Ped.

f *cresc.*

Ped.

SANCTUS

Ho - san - na in the high - est.

Choir

mp Bless - ed is he who comes   in the

name   of   the   Lord.   Bless - ed is he who

All

comes in the name of the Lord.

f Ho - san - na   Ho - san - na

(add)   (add)

*Ho - san - na.

ff Ho - san - na in the high - est.

ff

* Optional Soprano descant

ACCLAMATIONS

Christ has died, Christ is ris - en, Christ will come a - gain.

A - men, a - men, a - men.

AGNUS DEI

For the Cathedral and Abbey Church of St Alban and its Diocese

THE ST ALBANS SETTING

Alan Ridout

KYRIE

GLORIA

Glo - ry to God in the high - est, and peace to his peo - ple on earth. Lord__ God,__ heav'n - ly King, al - migh - ty God and Fa - ther, we wor - ship you, we__ give you thanks, we praise you for your__ glo - ry.

Lord, Je - sus Christ, on - ly Son of the Fa - ther,

Lord God, Lamb of God, you take a - way the sin of the world: have

mer - cy on us; you are seat - ed at the right hand of the

Fa - ther re - ceive our___ prayer. For

you a-lone are the Ho-ly One, you a-lone are the

Lord, you a-lone are the Most High, Je-sus

Christ, with the Ho-ly Spi-rit, in the glo-ry of God the

Fa-ther. A-men.

rit.

THE GOSPEL

Glo - ry to Christ our Sa - viour

Praise to Christ our Lord.

SANCTUS

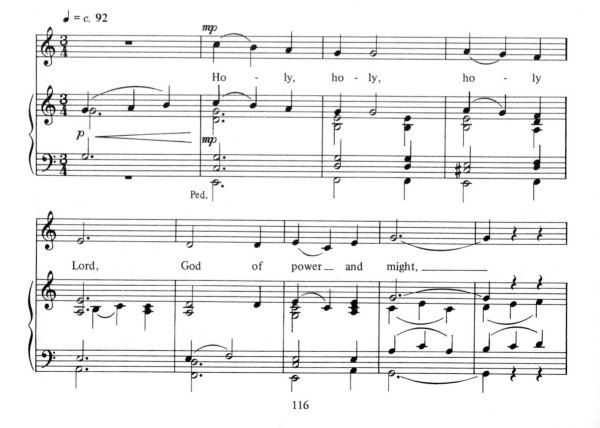

Ho - ly, ho - ly, ho - ly

Lord, God of power and might,

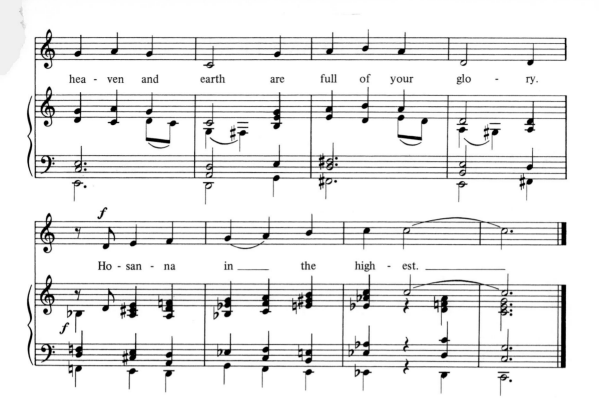

heaven and earth are full of your glory.

Ho - san - na in the high - est.

BENEDICTUS

Bless - ed is he who comes in the name of the Lord.

Ho - san - na in the high - est.

ACCLAMATIONS

Christ has died: Christ is ri-sen: Christ will come a-gain.

Bless-ing and ho-nour and glo-ry and

power be yours___ for ev-er and ev-er. A-men.

AGNUS DEI

Je-sus, Lamb of God: ___ have

mer- cy on us. Je - sus, bear- er of our sins: have

mer- cy on us. Je - sus, re- deem- er of the

world: give us your peace.

DISMISSAL

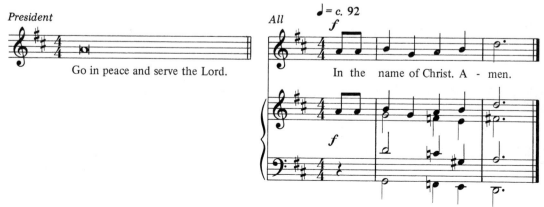

President

Go in peace and serve the Lord.

All   ♩ = c. 92

In the name of Christ. A - men.